JOHN MILNE

Money For a Motorbike

MACMILLAN

BEGINNER LEVEL

Founding Editor: John Milne

The Macmillan Readers provide a choice of enjoyable reading materials for learners of English. The series is published at six levels – Starter, Beginner, Elementary, Pre-intermediate, Intermediate and Upper.

Level control

Information, structure and vocabulary are controlled to suit the students' ability at each level.

The number of words at each level:

Starter	about 300 basic words
Beginner	about 600 basic words
Elementary	about 1100 basic words
Pre-intermediate	about 1400 basic words
Intermediate	about 1600 basic words
Upper	about 2200 basic words

Vocabulary

Some difficult words and phrases in this book are important for understanding the story. Some of these words are explained in the story and some are shown in the pictures. From Pre-intermediate level upwards, words are marked with a number like this: ...[3]. These words are explained in the Glossary at the end of the book.

It was the month of June and the weather was beautiful. Stuart left school. He was on holiday. But he was not happy. He did not have a motorbike.

Stuart was seventeen years old. He left school, but he did not start work. All his mates started work immediately, but Stuart did not want to work. He wanted a long holiday and he needed a motorbike.

Stuart lived in Leeds – a big city in the North of England. Leeds is a busy city – full of offices, shops and factories. It's not a good place for a holiday.

Martin, a friend of Stuart's, worked in a garage. Martin had a bike for sale. It was a beauty – a Japanese Suzuki. Martin wanted £350 for the bike, but Stuart did not have £350. He didn't have any money.

Stuart went and looked at the bike every day. It was a beauty. He wanted to buy it.

'Where can I find £350?' Stuart asked himself.

Stuart left the garage and walked back home. His house was in Blenheim Street, near the university. There were lots of old, empty houses in Blenheim Street.

The university was one of the biggest in England. The university often bought land and buildings. Most of the old houses in Blenheim Street belonged to the university.

Some of these houses had been empty for years. Stuart often searched through them. Sometimes he found old books and gramophone records.

'One day,' he told himself, 'I'll find something valuable.'

There was a large house at the corner of Blenheim Street. Its owner – a rich, old woman – had died a few days ago. The university bought the house immediately.

Now the house was empty. There was wood across the front door and the windows were broken.

Someone looked out of a window. It was a man of about twenty. He had long hair and was wearing a headband. He looked strange.

He was a squatter. Squatters live in old, empty houses and they don't pay any rent.

The stranger waved to Stuart. He wanted to speak to Stuart.

'What does he want?' Stuart asked himself.

Frank walked off slowly down the street. His head was bent forward and he was looking down at the pavement. He was about twenty, but he looked much older.

Frank went round the corner and Stuart turned towards the house. It looked interesting.

The window was low – quite near the ground. The street was empty. Stuart put one leg over the window sill and looked inside.

Outside the sun was shining brightly. Inside the house it was dark. Stuart stood for a few moments and waited. Slowly the inside of the room became clearer.

There was a calendar on the wall. Lots of old newspapers were lying around on the floor. There was a mattress against the far wall. It looked new.

Stuart looked up and down the street. There was no one around. He quickly climbed into the room.

Stuart walked to the middle of the room and kicked away the old newspapers. There was nothing underneath them. There was no carpet and the floorboards were covered with dirt.

Stuart took the calendar down from the wall. It was an old one – five years old. No one had changed it for five years. Then Stuart remembered. The owner of the house – the old woman – had been ill for a long time. She hadn't got out of her bed for five years.

The mattress was leaning against the far wall. Stuart went over and looked at it carefully. It was a good mattress.

Stuart picked up the mattress and turned it over carefully. There was some stitching along one side – about ten centimetres long. Stuart held the mattress between his knees and took out a small knife.

Stuart cut the stitches carefully and then put his hand in the hole. He felt a bundle of newspapers and pulled it out. He quickly unwrapped it. Inside the bundle of newspapers there were some banknotes.

Suddenly Stuart heard a voice. It was Frank.

'Hey – Stuart – where are you?' Frank was shouting.

Stuart quickly wrapped up the money inside the newspapers. He held the bundle behind his back.

'I'm in here, Frank,' he shouted.

Frank came up to the window and looked into the room.

'What are you doing in there?' Frank asked.

'Nothing,' replied Stuart. 'I'm looking around.'

Frank climbed into the room and came closer to

Stuart. Stuart moved to the wall. He held the bundle of newspapers behind his back.

Frank looked round the room. He didn't see Stuart's knife on the floor.

'You haven't taken anything, have you?' asked Frank.

'I haven't taken anything of yours,' replied Stuart.

'You've moved this mattress,' said Frank.

Frank picked up the mattress and turned it over carefully. Then he saw the hole in the side.

15

Stuart remembered the motorbike. He needed the money. He was going to keep it. It was his money, not Frank's.

Frank was holding Stuart's knife in his hand. He came nearer to Stuart.

'Give me those newspapers,' he said again.

Stuart had an idea.

'There's something else in the mattress,' he said to Frank. 'There was something under the newspapers. It's still there.'

Frank looked at Stuart for a few moments. He didn't believe him at first.

'Look and see,' said Stuart.

Frank put the knife down on the floor. He picked up the mattress and put his hand deep in the hole.

Stuart did not wait for a moment. He turned and jumped out through the window into the street.

He ran quickly. There was a turning on the right. Stuart ran round the corner. He heard a shout behind him. It was Frank.

Round the corner, there was another old, empty house. It had a large garden on one side. Thick bushes had grown all over the garden. Stuart jumped over the low wall. He ran for a few metres and then hid under some bushes.

Stuart heard more shouting and footsteps. The footsteps became louder, then they stopped. Stuart waited silently. He did not breathe. Then the footsteps started once again.

Stuart laughed quietly to himself.

Frank had quickly picked up Stuart's knife. He jumped out of the window after him.

Frank saw Stuart. He was running round the corner. Frank ran after him and turned the corner. But the street was empty.

Frank stopped for a few moments and looked around. He noticed the old garden.

'Perhaps he's in there,' thought Frank.

But everything in the garden was quiet. Frank saw nothing. There was another corner farther down the street.

Frank started running again. He was still holding Stuart's knife.

Stuart was happy. He had escaped from Frank with the money.

Stuart sat up under the bushes and opened out the newspapers. The banknotes were wrapped tightly together. Stuart unwrapped them and counted them carefully.

'Ten, twenty, thirty . . . three hundred and twenty, three hundred and twenty-five.'

Stuart had found £325. And Martin wanted £350 for his motorbike.

It was cool in the garden and Stuart lay back under the bushes.

I'll wait here for half an hour, thought Stuart. Then I'll go to Martin.

It was now nearly twelve o'clock. The day was getting much hotter. A police car was parked in a side street.

There were two policemen in the car. The sergeant – a fat, round-faced man – was half asleep. The other policeman was younger and taller. He was a constable.

Suddenly, the constable sat up. He had seen something strange.

'Wake up, sergeant,' he shouted. 'Look over there.'

'Where? What?' asked the sergeant still half asleep.

'Over there – someone's running with a knife,' replied the constable. 'The man's gone mad. It's this heat.'

'Quick – get out and catch him,' said the sergeant.

The two policemen jumped out of their car. Frank saw the policemen. He threw Stuart's knife away and started to run. The constable soon caught him and held his arm tightly.

The sergeant found the knife in some long grass. The constable took Frank towards the police car. The sergeant came up to them. He was holding the knife.

'Oh – it's you,' the sergeant said to Frank.

'Where are you taking me?' asked Frank.

'To the police station,' replied the constable.

'But I haven't done anything. The money was mine. That guy took it. What's his name? Stuart . . . Stuart took it.'

'Who's Stuart?' asked the constable.

'I met him in an old house,' replied Frank.

'Where you found the money?' asked the sergeant.

'Yes, I found it inside a mattress,' said Frank.

'Who's got the money now?' asked the sergeant.

'That guy – Stuart. He ran away with it.'

'So, now we have to find Stuart,' said the constable.

Stuart waited in the garden for half an hour. It was getting hotter. It was nearly twelve o'clock.

I'll have to move now, thought Stuart. Martin goes for his lunch at half past twelve.

Stuart looked out carefully from the bushes. The garden was empty. He hurried out of the garden onto the street. He walked towards Martin's garage.

Stuart did not see the police car. It stopped outside the garden a few moments later.

'Look in this garden,' Frank told the policemen. 'Perhaps he's hiding in here.'

26

The policemen got out of the car. Frank got out too. The constable held his arm tightly. The sergeant went into the garden. He looked around for some time. Then he came back. He was holding a bundle of newspapers.

'There's no one there,' the sergeant said. 'But I found these old newspapers.'

'That's them,' shouted Frank. 'Something was wrapped in those newspapers.'

Just then a motorbike drove up towards the police car.

'That's him,' shouted Frank excitedly. 'That's the guy. He's bought a motorbike with my money.'

'Stop,' the sergeant called to Stuart. 'Stop.'

Stuart did not see Frank.

'What do the police want?' Stuart asked himself. 'I haven't done anything wrong. I'm driving correctly.'

Stuart stopped the bike by the side of the road. He took off his helmet.

'Is that bike yours?' the sergeant asked him.

'Yes, it's mine,' replied Stuart. 'I bought it at the garage down the road.'

Then Stuart saw Frank.

'What have you told these cops?' Stuart shouted angrily at Frank.

'We'll all go to this garage,' said the sergeant.

They all walked back to Martin's garage.

A big, black cloud now covered the sun. It was beginning to rain.

'So, this lad paid you £325 for this bike,' the sergeant said to Martin.

Martin agreed.

'And where did you get this money?' the sergeant asked Stuart.

'I found it,' replied Stuart. 'I found it in a mattress. It was in an empty house.'

The sergeant took the money from Martin.

'We'll look after this money,' he said. 'You two can go now.'

'It's my money,' shouted Frank.

'Do you want to come to the police station with us?' asked the constable.

Frank walked away, still shouting.

'I'm sorry,' Martin said to Stuart. 'It's my bike again.'

'Not for long,' replied Stuart.

'What do you mean?' asked the sergeant.

'It has started to rain now,' replied Stuart. 'I don't want a holiday. I'm going to get a job. I'm going to save another £325 and buy that bike.'

Published by Macmillan Heinemann ELT
Between Towns Road, Oxford OX4 3PP
Macmillan Heinemann ELT is an imprint of
Macmillan Publishers Limited
Companies and representatives throughout the world
Heinemann is a registered trademark of Harcourt Education, used under licence.

ISBN 1–405072–44–X
EAN 978–1–405072–44–1

Text © John Milne 1976, 1992, 2002, 2005
First published 1976

Design and illustration © Macmillan Publishers Limited 2002, 2005

This edition first published 2005

Illustrated by Kim Harley
Original cover template design by Jackie Hill
Cover illustration by Chris Burke

Printed in Thailand

2009 2008 2007 2006
10   9   8   7   6   5   4   3